Violin Exam Pieces

ABRSM Grade 5

Selected from the syllabus from 2024

Nai

MW00800938

Date of exam

Contents

page

Violin consultant: Maureen Parrington
Footnotes: Philippa Bunting & Richard Jones (RJ)

The pieces listed above are just a selection of those on the syllabus that you can choose for your exam; the other options are listed on page 20.

Whether you are taking an ABRSM Practical or Performance Grade, pieces are at the heart of your exam; after all, playing an instrument is all about exploring, performing, and learning through repertoire.

While this book contains nine pieces in a range of styles, the full syllabus has a wealth of other exciting repertoire that we encourage you to explore – to find pieces that really inspire you, that you connect with musically and will enjoy learning, and that will allow you to perform to your very best. You can pick a mixture of pieces from this book and the wider lists if you like – you just need to have one piece from each list, A, B and C.

If you are taking a **Performance Grade**, you also need to prepare a fourth piece which is entirely your own choice. Here you have even more freedom to choose music that really speaks to you, that you want to communicate to others, and that successfully completes your programme. It can be from the syllabus lists, or somewhere else entirely. Just be sure to check the 'Selecting Repertoire' section of the Performance Grades syllabus for important requirements and options for the own-choice piece (like standard and minimum length) and the programme of four pieces overall. Finally, you need to decide what order to play your pieces in and how you, the performer, will take your audience from the very first to the very last note, including moving from one piece to another, so that the performance forms a complete musical journey.

The separate syllabuses are available at **www.abrsm.org**. Whether taking a Practical or Performance Grade, enjoy exploring the possibilities on offer!

First published in 2023 by ABRSM (Publishing) Ltd,
a wholly owned subsidiary of ABRSM, 4 London Wall Place,
London EC2Y 5AU, United Kingdom
© 2023 by The Associated Board of the Royal Schools of Music
Distributed worldwide by Oxford University Press

Music origination by Moira Roach
Cover by Kate Benjamin, James Pike & Andy Potts, with thanks to
Sutton Music Service
Printed in England by Caligraving Ltd, Thetford, Norfolk, on materials
from sustainable sources. P15917

Giga

from Sonata in D, Op. 25 No. 5

Edited by Richard Jones

Michel Corrette
(1707–95)

Michel Corrette was a French composer who also worked as a music teacher and organist. He wrote many music instruction books, including the violin treatise *L'école d'Orphée* (1738), which contrasts the French and Italian styles of the day.

This piece shows a French composer writing in the Italian style. The *giga*, an Italian variant of the French *gigue*, is characterised by its fast quaver motion in compound time. Corrette's cross-hands passages (keyboard part bars 5, 40, 66 and 80) recall the Giga from J. S. Bach's keyboard Partita in B flat. Corrette, however, combines them with a freely imitative violin part that alternates between the highest and lowest strings of the instrument. Another link with Bach is the scoring for obbligato keyboard – Corrette writes out his keyboard part in full (rather than using figured bass), just as Bach does in his six violin and keyboard sonatas, BWV 1014–19. RJ

Source: *Sonates pour le clavecin avec un accompagnement de violin*, Op. 25, Sonata No. 5, *Les jeux Olympiques* (Paris: l'auteur, Mme Boivin, Le Clerc, n.d.). All dynamics are editorial suggestions only. In the keyboard, the lower A in the left hand of bar 23 might be omitted to ease playing (cf. bars 78–9 and 90–1). In bar 77, keyboard, the upper octave notes a′ and A were omitted from the source in error; they have been added by the editor. In the violin part, 't' stands for trill (instead of the more usual ***tr***). The trills in bars 27, 28, 31 and 32 are editorial by analogy with those of the source. Slurs have also been added, in keeping with those of the composer, in bars 29, 31, 33–5, 36–9 and 56–7. The notation has been corrected in the closing bar of each half.

A:2

Allegro

Second movement from Sonata in F, Op. 1 No. 12, HWV 370

Edited by Richard Jones

attrib. G. F. Handel
(1685–1759)

In 1732 Handel's publisher John Walsh produced a corrected edition of the composer's solo sonatas; a note on the title page assured the public that 'This is more correct than the former edition'. Nevertheless, it includes two sonatas not actually by Handel, one of which – No. 12 in F, from which the above Allegro is taken – has become deservedly popular amongst violinists. All dynamics and slurs are editorial suggestions only. The Baroque technique used in bars 21 and 23, where a tune on one string is alternated with open string notes, is known as 'bariolage' and has the effect of creating maximum resonance. RJ

A:3

Giga

Fourth movement from Sonata in G minor, Op. 5 No. 6

Edited by and continuo realisation
by Richard Jones

J. B. Loeillet
(1688–c.1720)

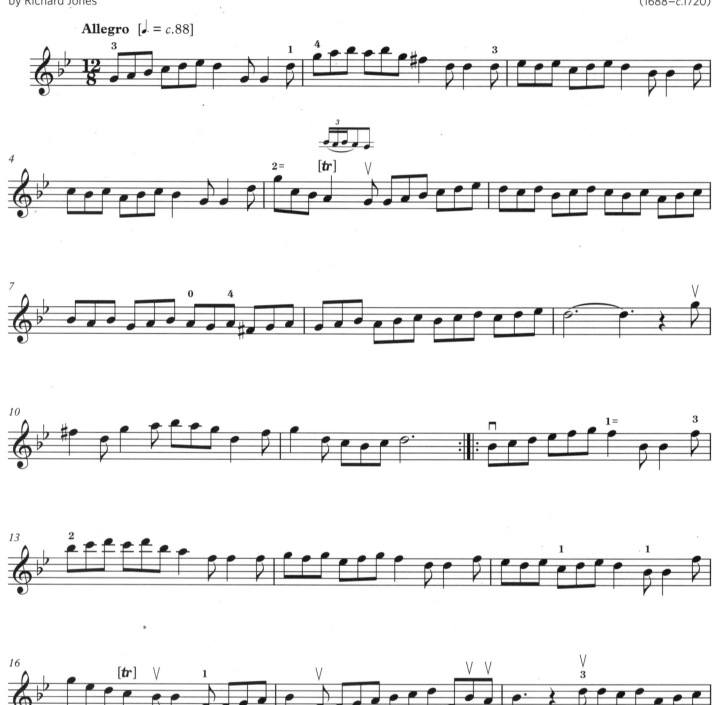

Jean Baptiste Loeillet was born into a Flemish family of musicians in Ghent (Belgium). He published five sets of sonatas. The last of them, Op. 5, is made up of two *livres* (books): *Livre premier* (from which this piece is taken) contains six sonatas for violin (or oboe or flute) and continuo; *Livre second* consists of six duet sonatas without continuo. Loeillet's sonatas are written in the French style of the period, intermingled with Italianate dance forms – *giga* is the Italian form of the French *gigue*. RJ

Source: first edition, *VI Sonates*, Op. 5, *Livre premier* (Amsterdam: Jeanne Roger, n.d. [1717]). There are no dynamics in the source, so players are free to invent their own dynamic schemes. All trills are editorial suggestions only. The accidentals at the second bass note of bars 19 and 20 are editorial. The last bass note of bar 23 is A in the source, not F♯, but cf. bars 4 and 15. The tie in the bass of bar 28 is editorial (cf. bars 8–9).

© 2023 by The Associated Board of the Royal Schools of Music

B:1

Romance

No. 1 from Two Romances

Elfrida Andrée
(1841–1929)

In the exam, the mute is optional, as is the IV (sul G) indication.

Composer, conductor and organist Elfrida Andrée was a significant figure in the musical history of her native Sweden, becoming the first female cathedral organist in Scandinavia when she took up that role at Gothenburg Cathedral in 1867. She was also the first Swedish woman to conduct a symphony orchestra. The restless melody in this Romance is full of longing and invites a singing legato sound, exploring the timbre of the instrument across its full range. Try to connect one bow to the next, listening to what happens between the notes as well as to the notes themselves. As you explore the sounds you can make, you are free to change the fingering to suit your own interpretation.

Source: *Två Romanser* (Stockholm: Abr. Hirsch, n.d. [1884]). The arpeggio signs in the piano part of bar 26a are editorial (cf. bar 1), as are the dynamics in the piano in bar 13 and the violin part in bar 25. In bar 31, the rhythm in the right-hand piano part is incorrect and has been altered here to match bar 30.

© 2023 by The Associated Board of the Royal Schools of Music

走西口 Zǒu Xī Kǒu

Leaving Home

B:2

Arranged by Zhou Long

Trad. Shanxi

This traditional folksong from Northern China has been arranged by the Chinese American composer Zhou Long, whose music is celebrated for its unique fusion of Chinese and Western musical sounds and traditions. The grace notes, harmonics and other details in this arrangement are integral to the style and should be observed. If you are not familiar with this style of music, listening to some examples will help you to feel how the music ebbs and flows, not necessarily remaining in strict tempo throughout. For the closing harmonic, rest your finger lightly on the G indicated by the diamond-shaped notehead. Although the arranger's metronome mark is ♩ = 60, students may prefer a slower tempo, for example ♩ = c.50.

B:3

A Nightingale Sang in
Berkeley Square

Arranged by Nikki Iles

Music by Manning Sherwin (1902–74)
Lyrics by Eric Maschwitz (1901–69)

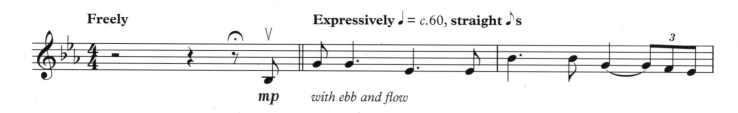

Gently swinging and a little more pace

slight rall.

Broadly, straight ♪s

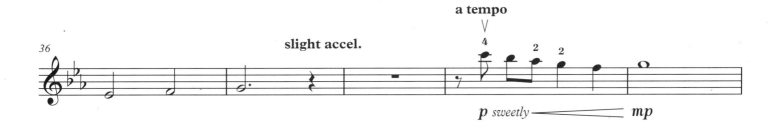

a tempo

slight accel.

big rall.

slight rall.

Written in 1939 as a stand-alone song, 'A Nightingale Sang in Berkeley Square' has captured the imagination of musicians ever since, establishing itself as a jazz standard and existing in numerous arrangements. The words of the first verse set the scene for what is one of the most popular romantic songs of the 20th century:

>That certain night, the night we met,
>There was magic abroad in the air,
>There were angels dining at the Ritz
>And a nightingale sang in Berkeley Square.

Musicians generally take an elastic approach to the song, and that is true in this arrangement as well: follow the contours of the melody and make each note really speak, without sticking to a strict tempo.

C:1

Tango Habanera

Barbara Arens
(born 1960)

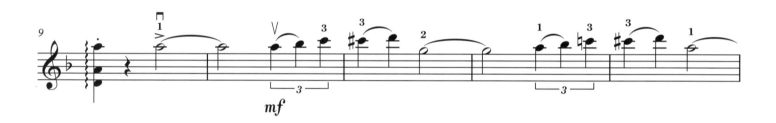

Barbara Arens is a dedicated piano teacher and composer with a passion for writing engaging, expressive pieces for students. In this piece, she brings to life a vibrant and energetic tango – a Latin American song and dance form, combining influences from different cultures. The tango is a highly dramatic dance, enhanced by strong eye contact and sharp, quick movements. This piece has plenty of intensity in the soaring melody, cut across by sharp staccato chords and accented notes.

D.S. al Coda

CODA

C:2

Moderato

First movement from Sonatine

Germaine Tailleferre
(1892–1983)

Germaine Tailleferre was at the heart of French artistic life as a member of the 'Les Six' group of composers, and as a friend of Maurice Ravel and Erik Satie, who once called her his 'musical daughter'. She credited Pablo Picasso with the best lesson in composition she had ever received, when he advised: 'constantly renew yourself; avoid using the recipes that you have already found'. A composer throughout her life, her prolific output included works for theatre, radio and film.

© 1974 by Gérard Billaudot Éditeur
14, rue de l'Échiquier – 75010 Paris

C:3

Czardas

No. 3 from *Hungarian Sketches*, Op. 23

Edited by Richard Jones

Gustav Hille
(1850 – c.1925)

Allegro [♩ = c.120]

f *appassionato*

molto rit.   a tempo

Born in 1850 in Jerichow, near Berlin, Gustav Hille became a pupil of the great violinist Joseph Joachim. He emigrated to America and taught from 1880 in Philadelphia, directing his own conservatory there from 1910. *Czardas* aims to recreate the fire and passion of traditional Hungarian folk-dance music. RJ

Source: *Bilder von der Puszta: Hungarian Sketches*, Op. 23 [London: Laudy & Co., 1906]. In the piano part, the last LH note in b. 105 has been changed from D♯ to E by analogy with b. 9.

This page may be photocopied to avoid the previous page turn.

Violin Exams
from 2024

Other pieces for Grade 5

		Composer	Piece	Publication
A	4	J. C. Bach	Presto (3rd movt from *Symphony No. 4*), arr. Wade	The Young Symphonist, Vol. 3 (Clifton Edition)
	5	Boyce	Allegro (1st movt from *Symphony No. 4 in F*), arr. Wade	The Young Symphonist, Vol. 3 (Clifton Edition)
	6	J. S. Bach	Bereite dich, Zion (from *Weihnachtsoratorium*, BWV 248), arr. K. & D. Blackwell	Bach for Violin (OUP)
	7	Gossec	Tambourin, arr. Nelson	Sheila M. Nelson's Classical Violinist (Boosey & Hawkes)
	8	Joachim Johow	Café classique (No. 5 from *Coffee & Violin*)	Joachim Johow: Coffee & Violin (Schott)
	9	Senaillé	Allegro (spiritoso) (4th movt from *Sonata No. 4 in D minor*)	Senaillé: Sonata in D minor (OUP *or* Schott)
	10	Leclair	Allegro (2nd movt from *Sonata in B minor*, Op. 2 No.11)	Französische Violinmusik der Barockzeit 2 (Henle)
	11	Mascitti	Giga	Grade by Grade, Violin Grade 5 (Boosey & Hawkes) *or* Sheila M. Nelson's Baroque Violinist (Boosey & Hawkes)
	12	Telemann	Allegro (2nd movt from *Sonata in G*, TWV 41:G1)	Telemann: 6 Sonatas for Violin (Schott)
	13	Vivaldi	Allemanda (2nd movt from *Sonata in F*, RV 20 Op. 2)	Vivaldi: 12 Sonatas for Violin, Op. 2 Book 1 (Schott) *or* Baroque Violin Pieces, Book 3 (ABRSM)
B	4	Bridge	Cradle Song, H. 96	Bridge: Three Pieces for Violin (Faber) *or* The Best of Grade 5 Violin (Faber)
	5	Ireland	Berceuse	Ireland: Berceuse for Violin (Stainer & Bell)
	6	attrib. Paradis	Sicilienne, arr. Dushkin	Paradis: Sicilienne for Violin or Cello (Schott) *or* Encore Violin, Book 3 (ABRSM)
	7	Pergolesi	Siciliano	Small Concert Pieces, Vol. 1 (EMB Zeneműkiadó)
	8	Rieding	Andante sostenuto (2nd movt from *Concertino in G*, Op. 24)	Rieding: Concertino in G, Op. 24 (Bosworth)
	9	Shostakovich	Elegie, arr. Fortunatov	Shostakovich: Albumstücke (Peters *or* Sikorski)
	10	Tchaikovsky	Waltz (from *Serenade for Strings*), arr. Huws Jones	Going Solo for Violin (Faber)
	11	Branscombe	An Old Love Tale, Op. 21 No.1, arr. Cooper *mute and sul G optional*	Violin Music By Women: A Graded Anthology, Vol. 3 Intermediate 2 (Sleepy Puppy Press)
	12	Sally Greenaway	Danza del Anhelo	Lyrical Violin Legends (Allegro)
	13	Joe Hisaishi	Departure (from *Kiki's Delivery Service*), arr. Shimazu	Joe Hisaishi: Studio Ghibli Songs for Violin, Easy-Intermediate (Yamaha)
C	4	Diana Burrell	The Secrets of the Dark Pool in the Pine Forest	Diana Burrell: The Secrets of the Dark Pool in the Pine Forest (UMP)
	5	Kodály	Intermezzo (from *Háry János*), arr. Kolman	Universal Violin Album, Vol. 3 (Universal)
	6	Timothy & Natasha Kraemer	Cossack Dance	Gypsy Jazz: Intermediate Level (Faber) *or* The Best of Grade 5 Violin (Faber)
	7	Lavildevan	Sugar with Cinnamon, arr. K. & D. Blackwell	Solo Time for Violin, Book 2 (OUP)
	8	Trad. Klezmer	Hava Nagila, arr. Stephen & Rowlands	Klezmer Fiddle Tunes (Schott) ◐
	9	Richard Wade	Barn Dance (from *Way Out West*)	Richard Wade: Way Out West (Queen's Temple Publications)
	10	Joe Hisaishi	A Town with an Ocean View (from *Kiki's Delivery Service*), arr. Shimazu	Joe Hisaishi: Studio Ghibli Songs for Violin, Intermediate (Yamaha)
	11	Ewa Iwan	Tarantella (from *Musical Journeys, Book 1*)	Ewa Iwan: Musical Journeys for Violin, Book 1 (PWM)
	12	Perlman	Hora-Hatikvah (1st movt from *Israeli Concertino*)	Perlman: Israeli Concertino (Boosey & Hawkes)
	13	Marceli Poplawski	Spanish Dance	Marceli Poplawski: Easy Pieces for Violin (PWM)

◐ Accompaniment printable from companion CD